M000074595

and the Sea

by Jake Harris
illustrated by Sarah Duke

Harcourt

SCHOOL PUBLISHERS

Printed in China

ISBN 10: 0-15-350448-X
ISBN 13: 978-0-15-350448-8

Ordering Options
ISBN 10: 0-15-350332-7 (Grade 2 Below-Level Collection)
ISBN 13: 978-0-15-350332-0 (Grade 2 Below-Level Collection)
ISBN 10: 0-15-357458-5 (package of 5)
ISBN 13: 978-0-15-357458-0 (package of 5)

4 5 6 7 8 9 10   0940   15 14 13 12 11 10 09

Abalone held tight to his rock in the sea. A bright fish peered up at him. Abalone felt a great sadness.

"Why do all the sea animals have beautiful colors except me?" he asked the Sea. "My entire shell is a dull gray, inside and out. I look just like the rock that I live on."

"I gave you a gray shell to hide you from your enemies," said the Sea. "You are never preyed upon because you are never noticed. Surely that must please you."

Abalone was still weighed down
with sadness. A bright blue crab was
scampering past him. "Look at Crab,"
he cried. "See how beautiful *she* is."

"Crab is never safe," the Sea said. "Big fish see her from a long way off. They make her their dinner. I have made you gray. I will not budge from my decision."

"Look at the beautiful rainbow fish," said Abalone. "He is the most majestic fish in the ocean."

"Yes, but people are always trying to catch him. He is so easy to see," said the Sea.

Abalone listened but did not hear. All he wanted was to be bright and beautiful.

Day after day, he asked and asked until the Sea gave in.

"Very well," said the Sea. "If I promise
to make you brightly colored, will you
promise never to bother me again?"

Abalone agreed. Then he discovered that Sea had tricked him.

The Sea had given him the brightest
shell of all. Its colors shone with pink,
blue, green, and silver. However, the
colors were on the inside of the shell.
The outside was still gray.

Abalone had promised never to bother the Sea again. He kept his word. To this day, you can only see his beautiful colors when his shell is washed up on the shore.

Think Critically

1. Why did Abalone want to have beautiful colors?

2. How do you know that the Sea was trying to protect Abalone?

3. Read page 5 again. What do you think *preyed upon* means?

4. What colors did the Sea give Abalone? Where were the colors?

5. Do you think the Sea did the right thing giving Abalone colors on the inside of his shell? Why or why not?

 **Language Arts**

Write a Short Story Write a short story about one of the characters from the book, such as Crab or the rainbow fish. Share the story with a friend.

School-Home Connection Tell a family member about *Abalone and the Sea.* Talk about different animals that live in the sea.

Word Count: 303